GCSE
AQA Business Studies
The Workbook

This book is for anyone doing **AQA GCSE Business Studies**.

It's full of **tricky questions**... each one designed to make you **sweat** — because that's the only way you'll get any **better**.

It's also got some daft bits in to try and make the whole experience at least vaguely entertaining for you.

What CGP is all about

Our sole aim here at CGP is to produce the highest quality books — carefully written, immaculately presented and dangerously close to being funny.

Then we work our socks off to get them out to you — at the cheapest possible prices.

Contents

AQA Unit 1 — Setting Up a Business

Section One — Starting a Business

Why Businesses Exist 1
Enterprise 2
Business Ownership Structures 3
Franchises 5
Aims, Objectives and Business Success 6
The Influence of Stakeholders 7
The Business Plan 8
Location of Production 9

Section Two — Marketing 1

The Marketing Mix 10
More About Marketing 11
Market Research 12
Products 13
Price — Demand and Supply 14
Promotion and Place 15

Section Three — Finance 1

Revenue, Costs and Profit 16
Sources of Finance 17
Starting a Business — Help and Support 18
Cash Flow 19
Cash Flow — Problems 20

Section Four — People in Business 1

Recruitment — Job Analysis 21
Recruitment — the Selection Process 22
Financial Rewards 23
Non-Financial Rewards 24
Employment and the Law 25

Section Five — Operations Management 1

Methods of Production 26
New Technology in the Workplace 27
Quality Assurance 28
Customer Service 29
Government Policy — Consumer Protection 30
New Technology — E-Commerce 31

AQA Unit 2 — Growing As a Business

Section Six — The Business Organisation

Growth of Firms — Internal Expansion 33
Growth of Firms — External Expansion 34
Effects of Expansion on Stakeholders 35
Business Ownership Structures 36
Social Influences 37
Multinational Firms 38

Section Seven — Marketing 2

Product — The Product Life Cycle 39
Product — Product Portfolios 40
Price — Pricing Strategies 41
Promotion 42
Place — Where the Product is Sold 43

Section Eight — Finance 2

Sources of Finance — Large Firms 44
The Trading, Profit and Loss Account 45
Profitability Ratios 46
The Balance Sheet — Net Assets 47
The Balance Sheet — Capital Employed 48
Liquidity Ratios 49
Analysis of Accounts 50

Section Nine — People in Business 2

Organisational Structure 51
Effects of Expansion — Communication 53
Staff Training 54
Staff Motivation and Retention 55

Section Ten — Operations Management 2

Specialisation and Interdependence 56
Methods of Production 57
Productivity 58
Effects of Expansion — Economies of Scale 59
Quality Management 60

Assessment Skills

Controlled Assessment 61
Exam Marks 63
Sample Exam Questions 66

Published by CGP

Editors:
Katie Braid
Helena Hayes
Andy Park
Dave Ryan
Michael Southorn

Contributors:
Peter Cunningham
Colin Harber Stuart
Tim Major

With thanks to Simon Little and Victoria Skelton for the proofreading.

ISBN: 978 1 84762 318 8

Groovy website: www.cgpbooks.co.uk

Printed by Elanders Ltd, Newcastle upon Tyne.
Jolly bits of clipart from CorelDRAW®

Government Statistics or National Statistics reproduced under the Terms of the Click Use Licence.
Source: National Statistics website: www.statistics.gov.uk.
Crown copyright material is reproduced with permission of the Controller, Office of Public Sector
Information (OPSI).
Source 2001 Census data supplied by the General Register Office for Scotland © Crown Copyright

Based on the classic CGP style created by Richard Parsons.

Why Businesses Exist

Q1 Which **two** of the following would be the **most likely** reasons why someone would want to start their own business?

a) So they can pay less income tax. ☐

b) The independence of being their own boss. ☑

c) To reduce the number of hours they have to work. ☐

d) They have a great idea for a product or service. ☐

e) To prove to their friends that they've got the drive to succeed. ☐

I'm afraid we're going to have to let you go.

You're not the boss of me.

Q2 Read the text below and then answer the following question.

> Karen Booth is opening a small sandwich shop in Nantwich, Cheshire. In her first year, Karen aims to break even. For the years after that, Karen has decided on a number of things she wants to achieve, some financial, and others non-financial.

Suggest one possible **financial** aim and one possible **non-financial** aim for Karen.

a) Financial aim: to break about above even ✓

b) Non-financial aim: to attract more customer to the business ✓

Q3 Complete the sentences below, using words or phrases from the box to fill in the spaces.

> cover their costs   non-financial   not-for-profit   financial   increase profits
>
> paid out to shareholders   private sector   put back into the business   help other people

a) Most businesses will only pursue ___non-finacial___ objectives if they will also ___increuce profits___ in the long run. ✓

b) ___Private sector___ organisations aim to make enough money to ___put back into the business___ ✓ *cover their costs* ✓

Any surplus is ___not-for-profit put back into the business___ ✓

Q4 How are social enterprises different from most businesses?

they want to make a social inpat instead of profit ✓ *Impact instead*

The existence of businesses — I have video evidence...

Or at least I did, until my mum recorded over it with one of her Sunday night gentle-comedy-dramas. Nothing too tricky on this first page — and now you're nicely warmed up, I reckon you should have a crack at page 2.

Enterprise

Q1 Tick whether each of the following statements about enterprise activity is **true** or **false**.

		True	False
a)	Enterprise involves identifying new business opportunities.	☑	☑
b)	Entrepreneurs often look for a gap in the market for a new product or service.	☐	☑
c)	It is extremely rare for a new business to fail.	☐	☐
d)	Entrepreneurs might help existing companies expand by coming up with new ideas.	☐	☐
e)	The reward for successful enterprise activity is profit.	☐	☐

Q2 Explain what is meant by taking a **calculated risk**.

the probability of you ~~ferly~~ failing ✗
- research and plan to make the probability of success high.
They also weigh up the consequences of failure.

Q3 Which **two** of the following qualities do you think are most important for an entrepreneur to have?

a) A willingness to study for a business qualification. ☐

b) The ability to learn from past mistakes. ☑

c) Willingness to be the owner of a large business. ☐

d) The ability to do complex financial calculations. ☑ ✗

e) Having the initiative to seize business opportunities. ☐ ✓

There must have been something wrong with my calculations. This wasn't supposed to happen.

Q4 Use the information in the box below to answer the following questions.

> In 2007, journalist Jake Harte set up his ethical shoe company, Harte & Sole after realising that there was a gap in the market for fashionable vegan-friendly and ethically produced shoes. After visiting many trade shows, he managed to convince several manufacturers to provide him with just the shoes he needs, in small quantities so he never needs to hold much stock at home, where he runs the business from a small office. Using his contacts as a journalist, Jake was able to get the endorsement of several popular celebrities and has since seen his profits grow month after month.

a) Explain what made Jake's idea a **good business idea**.

It was a gap in the market ✓

b) Identify two enterprise skills shown by Jake.

1. Using contacts ✓

2. managed ✗ - use of small quantities to reduce space holding

Business Ownership Structures

Q1   Which **two** of the following are advantages of being a sole trader?

a) A sole trader has a partner to take care of running the business. ☐

b) Being a sole trader means you get to decide what to do with the profits of the business. ☑ ✗

c) It's easy and relatively cheap to start up as a sole trader. ✓ ☐

d) A sole trader can't lose more money than they've invested in the business. ☐

e) It's easy for the business to expand by making shares available for anyone to buy. ☐

Q2   Describe **two** disadvantages of being a sole trader.

1. *you can lose all you money u invested and your personal money as well due to unlimited liability*

2. *you work long hours.*

Q3   Explain how a partnership works, using the words in the box below.

two or more	decisions	profits	equal

A Partnership is two or more people. Partners have equal say in decisions and sharing of the profits.

Q4   Read the text below and then answer the question at the bottom of the page.

> Kate has just qualified as an accountant and wants to open an accountancy firm in her local town. Although she has managed to get a bank loan, she does not have a lot of money to put into the business. Somebody she studied with has suggested that they start the business together, as a partnership. Kate doesn't know this person well, and is unsure whether they share her vision for the business.

Discuss whether you think Kate should start her business as half of a partnership, or whether she should start up as a sole trader. Give reasons for your answer.

Advantages & disadvantages of partnership.

Advantages & disadvantages of a sole trader

> Hopefully you'll have lots to write about for this question — so find yourself a piece of paper to put your answer on.

Soul trading — I swapped mine for a 63" plasma screen...

All the stuff on this page is pretty straightforward, I reckon. Make sure you know the differences between sole traders and partnerships and the advantages and disadvantages of each — it's bound to come in handy.

Business Ownership Structures

Q1 Lisa and Paul have both written a definition of limited liability. Whose definition is correct?

> The maximum amount that the owners of a business can lose if the business fails is equal to the amount they have invested in the business.

Lisa

> Limited liability means that the maximum amount the owners of a business can lose if the business fails is equal to how much their shares are currently worth.

Paul

...... ~~Paul~~ ...... is correct.

LISA is correct

Q2 Describe **two** disadvantages of setting up a business as a private limited company rather than as a sole trader or partnership.

1. They can take your stuff *goods* if you go in debt ✗ They are expensive to set up
2. They are Legally obliged to publish its accounts every year

Q3 Noah has set up a private limited company selling sports memorabilia. Which **two** of the following are the **most likely** reasons that Noah set up his business as a private limited company?

a) He wanted to be the only owner of the business. ☐
b) He thought he could raise lots of money on the Stock Exchange. ☒
c) If the business fails, he will only be liable for the money he invested. ☑ ✓
d) It's the cheapest and easiest way to start up a business. ☐
e) He thought it would be a less risky way of starting his business. ☑ ✓

Q4 Read the text below and then answer the question that follows.

> Sid and Fred own Deeply Dishy Ltd. — a firm which installs TV aerials. The demand for installation has fallen over the last six months. They have outstanding debts with their aerial supplier and are unsure whether they'll be able to pay their staff at the end of each month.

Are Sid and Fred personally liable for the firm's debts? Explain your answer.

Think about the ownership structure of Deeply Dishy.

- They are not personally liable for the debts
- Deeply Dishy Ltd is liable for its own debt as a legal entity

Franchises

Q1 Frank is opening a franchise of Kolestro-Burger, a fast food company.

a) Explain what is meant by a 'franchise'.

a company which allow indavisuals to carry there (their) product or use their trade mark for a fee.

b) Explain why companies such as Kolestro-Burger may choose to operate as a chain of franchises.

So the (their) product is international ? ✗
— The business model has been proven to be successful
— Support is given with marketing, training and accounting

c) Which **two** of the points below are benefits to Frank of opening a franchise? Tick the correct answers.

i) Frank doesn't need to pay any money to Kolestro-Burger to set up the business. ☐
ii) Frank will receive training on how to run the franchise. ☑ ✓
iii) The day-to-day running of the business is handled by somebody else. ☐
iv) Marketing and advertising of products will all be done by Kolestro-Burger. ☑ ✓
v) Frank gets to make his own decisions about the direction his franchise takes. ☐

d) Why might banks be more willing to lend Frank money to start a franchise than if he was starting a business making and selling his own products? *(proven to be a success)*

because the product is well known and they will know it will make money ✓

e) How might the reputation of Kolestro-Burger be affected by how Frank runs his franchise?

the Reputation will increase as its seen by more people ✗
If run well the reputation will improve but it run badly the reputation will suffer.

f) What are the drawbacks for Frank of operating as a franchise?

he will have to pay the company every month, wont make hes (his) own decisons for the business ✓

Burger sales have risen. In an unconnected event, the dotted line shows the nation's average cholesterol level over the same period of time.

I'll have a hamburger and large franchise please...

One benefit of this page is that you've had a chance to practise your franchise knowledge. One drawback is that you're probably feeling quite hungry now. I am. Why not go and treat yourself to a biscuit. Or two.

Aims, Objectives and Business Success

Q1 What is the difference between the **aims** and **objectives** of a business?

....

....

....

Q2 Which of the following best supports the claim that a business has met its objective of behaving in an ethical way?

a) The firm now markets itself as a morally responsible business. ☐

b) The business now gets all its raw materials from fair trade sources. ☐

c) 85% of the firm's customers are happy with the standard of customer service they receive. ☐

d) The business has made record profits, and some of the shareholders would like to donate a portion of the profits to charity. ☐

Q3 Describe how a business could use its objectives to measure its financial performance over a year.

....

....

....

Q4 Alan runs a fruit and veg shop. Last year, his shop had sales of £90,000 and made a profit of £7,000. The table below shows some of his aims for this year. For each of his aims, write a suitable objective.

	Aim	Objective
a)	Increase sales	....
b)	Increase customer satisfaction	....
c)	Reduce the shop's environmental impact	....

The Influence of Stakeholders

Q1   Define the term 'stakeholder'.

....

....

Q2   Different stakeholders will have different opinions about what a firm's objectives should be. Fill in the table below to suggest what a firm's suppliers and the government might think the firm's objectives should be. Explain your answers.

Stakeholder	Think the firm's objectives should be...	Explanation
Suppliers	....	....
Government	....	....

Q3   Steve has recently bought a pub in a quiet residential area of town.
State how each of the following could affect both the **business** and its **wider stakeholders**.

a)   The pub plays loud music until the early hours of the morning most nights.

....

....

....

b)   The drinks are cheaper than other pubs in the area.

....

....

....

c)   The workers are paid well and have lots of benefits.

....

....

....

The Business Plan

Sam wants to start a business manufacturing and selling herbal self-tanning products. Sam's bank has told him that he must write a business plan before they will give him a loan to start his business.

Q1   A good business plan contains a number of different sections, shown below. Write a description of each section in the boxes below. (You shouldn't try to write Sam's business plan in the boxes.)

Personal details

....

....

Mission statement

....

....

....

Objectives

....

....

....

Product description

....

....

Production details

....

....

Staffing requirements

....

....

Finance

....

....

Q2   Does a good business plan guarantee that Sam's business will be successful? Explain your answer.

Sorry — I seem to have run out of page here. You'll have to grab yourself some paper to scribble the mini-essay answer to this question.

Location of Production

Q1   Roy and Hayley have decided to set up a sandwich shop in a busy city centre.
Identify and explain **two** factors they may have considered when deciding where to locate.

1. ....

....

2. ....

....

Q2   Explain why some firms may choose to locate closer to their customers than to their suppliers.

....

....

....

Q3   Give **one** advantage and **one** disadvantage of locating your business near to similar businesses.

Advantage: ....

....

Disadvantage: ....

....

Q4   Read the information below and answer the question that follows.

> Lion-Witch Ltd. make flat pack wardrobes which they sell over the internet. They want to
> expand their business by building a new factory. There are two possible locations.

Taketon

- area of high unemployment
- close to wood-processing plant
- close to motorway

Thatborough

- close to a large city
- similar businesses in the area
- good communication links

Use the information above to recommend **one** of the locations to Lion-Witch Ltd. Justify your answer.

subsidies   bulk-reducing   recruitment
labour   wages   suppliers

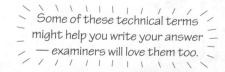

Some of these technical terms
might help you write your answer —
examiners will love them too.

Gary, Howard, Jason or Mark — decisions, decisions...

Make sure you know all the factors influencing the choice of location for a firm. Examiners will feel all warm
and fuzzy inside if you can identify which factors are important to different businesses, bless 'em.

The Marketing Mix

Q1   There are four Ps which together make up the **marketing mix** — product, price, promotion and place. Which **two** of the following statements are most important to the marketing mix?

a)   The product should include new technology.   ☐

b)   The product should be priced as cheaply as possible.   ☐

c)   Promotion should make potential customers aware that the product exists.   ☐

d)   The promotion for a product should be seen by everybody in the population.   ☐

e)   The product should be available in places convenient for people in the target market.   ☐

f)   The product should be available to buy in High Street shops.   ☐

Q2   Which of the following is the most important factor when making a product? Tick the correct box and explain your answer.

The product should satisfy customers' needs or wants.   ☐

The product should be cheap to make.   ☐

I know what you want, boys. You want to buy this car...

Explanation: ....

....

....

Q3   In some situations, some Ps in the marketing mix may be more important than others.

a)   Give an example of a situation where customers may choose to buy a particular **product** even though competing products have a lower **price**.

....

....

b)   Give an example of a situation where customers may choose to buy from a more distant store rather than a closer one.

....

....

Sales of this product have been poor in recent years...

Q4   Explain why a business might need to adapt its marketing mix over time.

....

....

....

....

The four Ps — easy P-sy if you ask me...

The marketing mix is like a rock band.   If all four Ps are playing in harmony, they make beautiful marketing music.   If one's playing off the beat, the whole thing sounds awful and nobody wants to buy their albums.

More About Marketing

Q1   A firm that sells products or services will have a **marketing strategy**.

a)   What is the purpose of a marketing strategy?

....

b)   Why is it important for a firm to analyse its strengths and weaknesses before deciding on a strategy?

....

....

Q2   Sonja is planning to open a new pub which will also serve cooked meals. She researches
the food offered by other pubs in the town and finds that very few of them offer a good
selection of vegetarian food. Sonja thinks she has found a **gap in the market**.

a)   Explain what is meant by a 'gap in the market'.

....

....

b)   Discuss how this gap in the market could affect Sonja's prices and promotion.

....

....

....

Q3   Explain why it is important for a business to find out about each of the following things before
entering a new market, and how having this information might help the firm spot a gap in the market.

a)   The **type of customers** who buy competing products.

....

....

....

b)   The **prices** of competing products.

....

....

....

c)   The **places** that competing products are sold.

....

....

....

Market Research

Q1 Explain why it is important for businesses to conduct **market research** before launching new products.

I can't wash up now, darling — I'm researching football data.

....

....

Q2 Market research can be either **primary** or **secondary**.

a) Explain the difference between primary and secondary market research.

....

....

I asked Leanne for her vital statistics.

Data?

Nah, we're just friends.

b) Which of the following are **disadvantages** of using secondary research?

i) It needs a large sample group to give meaningful results. ☐

ii) It is not always relevant to the needs of the business. ☐

iii) It's very time consuming to collect data. ☐

iv) The data may be out of date. ☐

v) The research may not be about the firm's products. ☐

Q3 Jackie runs a small business selling and delivering sandwiches.
She selects a sample of her potential customers to take part in a telephone survey.

a) Why might Jackie choose to survey a small sample of people rather than a large sample?

....

b) Explain why using a small sample might mean that Jackie's results are not accurate.

....

....

Jackie decides to do some secondary market research to support the results of her survey.

c) Give an example of a method of secondary market research.

....

d) Explain why a small business might prefer using secondary market research to primary research.

....

....

Research for the hero inside yourself...

If you don't research your market, it's likely that you'll end up trying to sell them something they don't want. Now, who wants to buy a framed print of that brilliant joke above about researching football data? Anyone?

Products

Q1 Businesses may be **market-driven** or **product-driven**.

a) Explain what a market-driven business would do before making a product.

....

....

b) Explain why a market-driven approach is often better than a product-driven approach.

....

....

Q2 Gloria has worked for a large toy-making business for ten years. She wants to use her experience to set up her own toy business. She needs to decide on a suitable product to make.

Give **two** reasons why a videogame console would **not** be a good choice of product for Gloria's new business.

1. ....

....

2. ....

....

Q3 Decide if each of the following statements is true or false.

	True	False
a) Niche markets are often ignored by larger firms, providing small businesses with opportunities.	☐	☐
b) Small business can do more market research, so they can make sure their products are always things that people want.	☐	☐
c) Small businesses find it easier to adapt their products to meet customers' needs.	☐	☐

Q4 Explain why it could be difficult for a large clothes manufacturer to offer tailor-made suits.

....

....

....

....

Didn't you get my text? We decided to go with the Tinker, Tailor theme instead...

Aww man. I even brought my YMCA CD.

Ice-cream vans — they must be product driven...

I had the great idea of selling ice over the internet. Didn't really work out though, my assets were always too liquid. Get it? Too *liquid*. Like they'd melted. Never mind — business studies jokes are never funny.

Price — Demand and Supply

Q1 Here is a list of statements about the laws of demand and supply.
Tick the pair of statements which are **both** correct.

LAW OF DEMAND	LAW OF SUPPLY	
A: Demand increases when price increases	Supply increases when demand increases	☐
B: Demand decreases when price increases	Price increases when supply increases	☐
C: Demand increases when price decreases	Supply increases when price increases	☐
D: Demand increases when supply decreases	Supply increases when demand decreases	☐

Q2 Jerome is the manager of Disherspooner, a small business that makes crockery and cutlery. He is thinking about reducing the price of the business's products. Suggest **two** reasons why demand for the firm's products would change.

1. ....

....

2. ....

....

Q3 Products reach an **equilibrium** price in certain types of market.

a) The graph below shows how equilibrium is related to **supply** and **demand**. Some parts of the graph have been labelled with numbers. Write the correct label next to the corresponding number below.

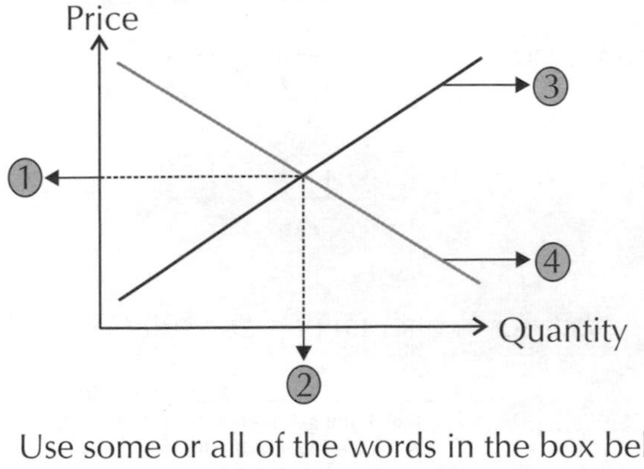

Price / Quantity graph with labels 1, 2, 3, 4

① ....

② ....

③ ....

④ ....

b) Use some or all of the words in the box below to explain why equilibrium price is reached.

supply   demand   shortage   surplus   reduce   increase   equilibrium

Make sure you use the right technical terms in the exam — it's worth marks.

....

....

....

....

Promotion and Place

Q1 Write down **two** ways that advertising can be used to help a firm increase sales.

1. ....

2. ....

Q2 Leah runs a small IT consultancy business — she gives advice and support to local businesses and residents on their computing needs. Leah has a limited advertising budget. Suggest **three** suitable and cost-effective ways she could advertise her business.

Coffee? Check. Doughnuts? Check. Advertising ideas? Erm... Ooh, those doughnuts look good.

1. ....

....

2. ....

....

3. ....

....

Q3 Motherload Ltd is a small business that sells products for babies and small children. Two examples of advertisements are given below. For each example, say whether it is likely to reach Motherload Ltd's **target audience**, and explain your answer.

a) Advertisements in local primary school newsletters/magazines.

Likely to reach Motherload's target audience?　　Yes ☐　　No ☐

Explanation: ....

....

b) Advertisements on a local radio station that plays songs from the 1950s and 1960s.

Likely to reach Motherload's target audience?　　Yes ☐　　No ☐

Explanation: ....

....

Q4 Hanif is starting a new business selling collectable CDs and records. Explain **two** advantages that selling online could have for Hanif's business.

1. ....

....

2. ....

Revenue, Costs and Profit

Q1 Draw lines to join each term to its description on the right.

Indirect costs	Expenses attributed to making a particular product.
Direct costs	The general overheads of running a business.

Q2 The box below contains several **fixed** and **variable** costs. Put each cost into the correct column of the table.

How much?!

factory labour   management salaries   office rent

machinery running costs   telephone bills   raw materials

Fixed cost	Variable cost
....	....
....	....
....	....

Q3 Define each of the terms below.

a) Revenue: ....

....

b) Average cost: ....

....

c) Profit: ....

....

Q4 A company makes 50,000 gift bags at a total cost of £17,500. All 50,000 are sold at £1.50 each. Tick whether the following statements are true or false.

		True	False
a)	The firm's total revenue is £50,000.	☐	☐
b)	The average cost of making each bag is 35p.	☐	☐
c)	After subtracting total costs from revenue, the business is left with £57,500.	☐	☐
d)	If the selling price of each bag had been any lower, they would not have made a profit.	☐	☐
e)	The business makes a profit of £32,500.	☐	☐
f)	If only 25,000 bags had been sold, the business would not have made a profit.	☐	☐

Sources of Finance

Q1 Explain why a new business might need a source of start-up finance.

....

....

Q2 Name **five** sources of finance that are available to people starting up a new business.

1. .... 　 2. .... 　 3. ....

4. .... 　 5. ....

Q3 Explain why small businesses often face difficulties when trying to raise finance.

....

....

Q4 Choose **three** sources of finance available to small firms and describe the drawbacks associated with each source.

Source of finance	Drawbacks
....	....
....	....
....	....

Q5 James has decided to start a new business — he's going to open a market stall selling sports equipment. Recommend one source of start-up finance that James should consider. Explain why you've recommended this using some of the words in the box below.

interest　collateral　control　stake

Make sure you use the right technical terms in the exam — it's worth marks.

Source of finance ....

Reason ....

....

....

Starting a Business — Help and Support

Q1   Write down **two** ways that the government can benefit if more people start their own business.

a)   ....

....

b)   ....

....

Q2   Explain how government support can help a new business to get a bank loan.

....

....

Q3   Which of the following is a government agency that provides help and support to new businesses? Tick the correct answer.

The bank have been very good in helping me get my thievery business off the ground.

a)   Business Link   ☐

b)   Venture Capital Enterprises   ☐

c)   Department for Managerial Economies   ☐

Q4   Many banks have schemes for helping new businesses.

a)   Suggest one way in which a bank might help a new business.

....

b)   Give **two** reasons why a bank may choose to help new businesses.

1.   ....

2.   ....

Q5   Which of the following is a charity that was set up to support young entrepreneurs?

a)   Duke of Edinburgh's Award   ☐

b)   Prince's Trust   ☐

c)   Queen's Award for Enterprise   ☐

Q6   Explain what a chamber of commerce is, and what they do to help local businesses.

....

....

....

Cash Flow

Q1 Explain what is meant by each of the terms below.

a) Cash flow: ....

....

b) Credit terms: ....

....

Q2 Explain why using a cash flow forecast might be useful for a business.

....

....

Q3 Yoo Too Sunglasses Ltd. gives its customers 60 days credit. Complete their cash flow table below.

Cash Flow Statement — Yoo Too Sunglasses Ltd.							
£	April	May	June	July	August	September	October
Total orders this month (for payment in 60 days)	1000	1300	1400	1500	1300	400	300
Total receipts (cash inflow)	300	350	1000	1300		1500	1300
Total payments (cash outflow)	1000	1200	1300		1250	300	200
Net cash flow	-700		-300	-50	150	1200	1100
Bank balance at start of month	1300	600		-550	-600	-450	750
Bank balance at end of month	600	-250	-550	-600	-450	750	

Q4 What would be the **most** likely effect of an unexpected rise in the demand for sunglasses in November?

a) Yoo Too's total receipts in November would increase. ☐

b) Cash outflow would increase as Yoo Too make more sunglasses to meet demand. ☐

c) Yoo Too would insist on their customers paying for the products by cash. ☐

d) Sales of sunglasses in December would also rise. ☐

Q5 Suggest what action the firm could take to see them through their liquidity problem in the summer months.

....

....

Cash Flow — Problems

Q1 Explain how each of the following can be a cause of cash flow problems.

a) Overtrading ....

....

....

b) Insufficient market research ....

....

....

Q2 Which of the following is **not** a problem associated with poor cash flow?

a) Creditors might give the company stricter credit terms in the future. ☐

b) Creditors may take legal action to recover any debt for unpaid bills. ☐

c) Staff may not get paid on time — causing poor motivation. ☐

d) The business cannot take out short-term finance to solve the problem. ☐

I should've listened to the forecast.

Q3 Suggest **three** ways in which a business can improve its cash flow.

1. ....

....

2. ....

....

3. ....

....

Q4 Explain what may happen to a firm if its creditors take legal action to get their money back.

....

....

....

....

Problems with your flow? You need to drink more fluids...

I know what you're thinking — we've all got cash flow problems. Unfortunately, small businesses can't always rely on the bank of Mum and Dad to lend them a tenner when they're skint. Pity really.

Recruitment — Job Analysis

Q1   Firms need to decide whether each of their positions
should be filled by a **part-time** or a **full-time** worker.

a)   Suggest two reasons why a firm might choose to employ a part-time worker.

1. ....

2. ....

b)   Explain the benefits that employing full time workers might have for a business.

....

....

Q2   Sally is the manager of a small pub that includes a restaurant. Her head chef is leaving,
and nobody on her current staff can take on the role. State whether each of the following
would be a suitable way for Sally to find a new head chef, and explain your answers.

a)   Asking a business contact for a personal recommendation.   Suitable?   Yes ☐   No ☐

Explanation: ....

....

b)   Advertising the position in a local Job Centre.   Suitable?   Yes ☐   No ☐

Explanation: ....

....

c)   Advertising the position in the national press.   Suitable?   Yes ☐   No ☐

Explanation: ....

....

Q3   Give **two** advantages and **two** disadvantages to a business of advertising a vacancy internally.

a)   Advantages   1. ....

2. ....

b)   Disadvantages 1. ....

2. ....

Q4   Explain why a small firm might use an **agency** to help them find candidates for a job.

....

....

....

Recruitment — the Selection Process

Q1   A curriculum vitae (or CV) is sometimes used in the selection process for a job.

a)   Which type of firm is most likely to ask job applicants for a CV?

A small firm ☐   A large firm ☐   Firms of all sizes ask for CVs ☐

b)   Write down three things that might appear on a candidate's CV.

1. ....

2. ....

3. ....

Q2   Which **three** of the following statements about interviews are true? Tick the correct boxes.

a)   Interviewers should ask all candidates the same questions.   ☐

b)   It is common to ask candidates about their religious beliefs in interviews.   ☐

c)   Interviews usually test the skills that are needed for the job.   ☐

d)   Candidates may find it difficult to behave naturally in an interview.   ☐

e)   Interviews can be a good test of verbal and social skills.   ☐

Q3   Why might some businesses ask candidates to complete an application form rather than write a letter?

....

....

....

Q4   Explain what **references** are and why they are used.

....

....

Q5   Advertivision is a large company in London that produces television advertisements. The company is recruiting new staff to work on its design and production teams.

a)   Advertivision gives each candidate a skills test, an aptitude test and a group test. Join each type of test to its description.

Skills test	Tests teamwork, leadership and decision-making skills
Aptitude test	Tests the candidate's ability to do the job
Group test	Tests the candidate's potential to learn the job

b)   Explain why Advertivision might want to give the candidates these tests as well as interviewing them.

....

....

Financial Rewards

Q1   Explain the difference between **wages** and **salaries**.

....

....

Q2   The box below contains three methods used for paying workers. For each occupation
      in the table, decide which is the most appropriate method and explain your choice.

      time rate   piece rate   commission

	Occupation	Method of Payment	Explanation
a)	Train driver	....	....
b)	Textiles worker making hand-made cushions	....	....
c)	Double-glazing salesperson	....	....

Q3   Tick whether the following statements are **true** or **false**.

                                                                               True   False

a)   A bonus is a lump sum of money added to a worker's pay. ☐ ☐

b)   Temporary workers are sometimes paid more than permanent workers
      to make up for the lack of job security. ☐ ☐

c)   Commission is paid to a worker as a reward for working overtime. ☐ ☐

d)   Temporary staff are paid for a fixed period of a few weeks or months. ☐ ☐

Q4   Explain why an 18-year-old receptionist in a law firm is likely
      to receive lower pay than a solicitor working for the same firm.

....

....

....

Non-Financial Rewards

Q1 Describe **two** ways that a business benefits from having well-motivated staff.

1. ....

....

2. ....

....

Q2 Explain how training can increase the motivation of staff.

....

....

Q3 Barbara is the production manager in a factory that makes electronic goods. She uses non-financial rewards to motivate her staff — the names of these rewards are given in the box below. Write the correct name after each description below.

Job enlargement   Fringe benefit   Job enrichment

a) Workers are given vouchers for free meals
in the factory's canteen.   ....

b) Workers are given a wider range of tasks,
including responsibility for supervising other staff.   ....

c) Workers are given more tasks in different parts of the factory,
but they are not given extra responsibility.   ....

Q4 For each of the schemes below, describe how they can lead to a more motivated workforce.

a) Job enlargement: ....

....

....

b) Job enrichment: ....

....

....

Q5 Explain why some firms may use non-financial rewards rather than paying their staff bonuses.

....

....

....

Employment and the Law

Q1 Which **three** of these statements about employment rights are true?

a) Employees must be given a written contract of employment within two months of starting a job. ☐

b) The EU law limits the working week to 72 hours for most employees ☐

c) All staff should have a copy of the firm's disciplinary procedure. ☐

d) The government sets a national minimum wage for most workers, depending on their age. ☐

Q2 Give **one** advantage and **one** disadvantage that minimum wage law has for small businesses.

Advantage	Disadvantage
....	....
....	....
....	....

Q3 List **five** things about a candidate that, by law, employers are not allowed to **discriminate** against when recruiting new staff.

1. ....

2. ....

3. ....

4. ....

5. ....

Q4 Explain how a business might benefit from Health and Safety Law.

....

....

....

⚠ Not suitable for children under 36 months or management staff due to small parts.

Q5 What is the only reason why an employee can be made **redundant** from their job?

....

Q6 Ben is the manager of a restaurant. Steve works for Ben as a waiter. One evening, Steve accidentally drops a plate of food on the floor.

Uh-oh, spaghettios...

a) Is it legal for Ben to dismiss Steve for this? Yes ☐ No ☐

b) Explain your answer.

....

....

Methods of Production

Q1 Which **two** of these statements about business efficiency are true?

a) An inefficient business will have very low operating costs. ☐

b) Lower costs always result in high profits for a business. ☐

c) An efficient firm would have lower operating costs than an inefficient one with the same output. ☐

d) Efficient firms use fewer resources per item produced than inefficient firms. ☐

e) A business operating inefficiently must be using job production. ☐

Q2 Explain why a small business may choose to use a method of production that is **not** the most efficient possible.

....

....

....

Q3 Explain what is meant by **job production**.

....

....

....

Geppetto says I'm unique.

Q4 A particular sofa manufacturer sells to furniture stores and directly to the public.

a) The manufacturer offers a service where they use the job production method to manufacture sofas designed to an individual customer's specification.

Describe some of the advantages and disadvantages to the firm of offering such a service.

....

....

....

....

b) A furniture store has asked this manufacturer to produce a limited number of identical sofas. Explain why batch production might be a more suitable manufacturing method for these sofas.

....

....

....

New Technology in the Workplace

Q1 Most shops now use bar codes and electronic scanners.
Describe how using this technology benefits both the shop and the customer.

....

....

Q2 Which of the following statements about Computer Aided Design (CAD)
and Computer Aided Manufacture (CAM) is **not** true?

a) The software is used to create 3D computer models of designs. ☐

b) Productivity is often reduced as the software is less accurate than traditional methods. ☐

c) It is easy to make instant changes to the designs. ☐

d) Using them helps reduce human error and improves quality of the designs. ☐

Q3 Kathryn is a beautician. She has decided to open up her own salon.
Suggest **two** ways in which she could use computers to help run her business.

1. ....

....

2. ....

....

Q4 Explain **three** ways that increasing use of computers in businesses can have drawbacks for employees.

1. ....

....

2. ....

....

3. ....

....

Q5 Explain how using computers can help a business to reduce costs.

If you need help starting your answer — look at the words in the grey box. They'd be really good things to write about.

faster   information   accuracy   networks   efficient

Looks like we're out of space again. It's every man for himself, space-wise.

A fatal error has occurred while running funnygag.exe...

It's hard to dispute that computers have made life a lot easier for everyone — workplaces are much more efficient than back in the olden days. In fact, my life is now so efficient that my days only last 23 hours.

~~Qualtiy~~ ~~Qwality~~ _Quality Assurance_

Q1 Explain why a business needs to have quality checks on its **products**.

....

....

Q2 Explain why quality is important in these areas of a business.

Customer services: ....

....

Promotional materials: ....

....

Q3 Identify **two** expectations about the quality of a product customers might have.

1. ....

2. ....

Q4 Which of these statements about quality are **not** true?

a) The quality of a product can depend on the materials
   it is made from and the techniques used to make it. ☐

b) People are often prepared to pay more for higher quality products. ☐

c) Firms can sell products of any quality, as long as their price reflects the quality. ☐

d) A policy of quality assurance only affects a firm when it creates promotional materials. ☐

Q5 Explain why a firm may try to gain membership of a trade association,
even if this means they incur extra expense.

....

....

....

Q6 Why might a firm display in its marketing materials brief details of quality awards it has won?

....

....

Customer Service

Q1 Which **two** of the following statements about customer service are true? Tick the correct boxes.

a) Customers have expectations about the level of service they should receive. ☐

b) Poor customer service can result in customers switching to other brands. ☐

c) A business has little to gain from providing good customer service. ☐

d) Customer service is unimportant after a firm's product has been purchased. ☐

Q2 A firm sells electrical kitchen appliances through its website. Which of the statements below are examples of good customer service? Explain your answers.

a) (75% of the firm's products are dispatched within four days of the given dispatch date.)

Good customer service? Yes ☐ No ☐

Explanation: ....

....

b) (The firm pays all postage costs when customers need to exchange faulty items.)

Good customer service? Yes ☐ No ☐

Explanation: ....

....

Oh, hello — I think my new blender is slightly faulty.

c) (The firm's call centre currently responds to 80% of customer telephone enquiries.)

Good customer service? Yes ☐ No ☐

Explanation: ....

....

Q3 Customer service has benefits for businesses and their customers.

a) Explain how good customer service can 'add value' to a product in the eyes of a consumer.

....

....

b) Explain how an increase in a firm's spending on customer service can lead to an increase in profits.

....

....

All our operatives are currently busy — please hold...

Thanks for calling the Business Studies exam helpline. If you would like to enquire about customer service, press 1 now. *Beep*. Thanks — your call is important to us. You are currently 17th in a queue. *Dial tone*.

Government Policy — Consumer Protection

Q1 Which two of the following best describe **Sale of Goods Legislation**? Tick the correct boxes.

a) The legislation makes it illegal for sellers to over-charge their customers. ☐

b) The legislation makes it illegal for organisations to endorse products. ☐

c) The legislation makes it illegal to give a false description of a product. ☐

d) The legislation says that products should meet a basic standard of quality. ☐

e) The legislation says that products should be the best possible quality. ☐

Question box for sale
Length: 168.9 mm
Height: 6.6 mm
Colour: Pale blue
Uses: Highlights questions,
cures baldness.
Only £59.99

Q2 Sale of Goods Legislation says that products should be **fit for their purpose**.

a) What does it mean for a product to be fit for purpose?

....

b) Give two properties a DVD player would need to have in order to be fit for its purpose.

1. ....

2. ....

Q3 Explain why each of the following would be illegal under Sale of Goods Legislation.

a) Selling a pen that writes well, but leaks ink.

....

....

b) Selling a washing-up liquid that does not get dishes clean.

....

....

c) Selling ten bread rolls in a packet that is labelled as containing twelve rolls.

....

....

Q4 Sale of Goods Legislation gives customers **legal rights** to complain about unsatisfactory products.

a) List three things that customers can ask for if a product does not meet legal requirements.

1. .... 2. .... 3. ....

b) Explain how a business might be damaged if its products do not meet legal requirements.

....

....

....

New Technology — E-Commerce

Q1   What is meant by the term **e-commerce**?

....

Q2   Tick whether each of the following statements about e-commerce is true or false.

		True	False
a)	Products ordered online usually have to be paid for by cash.	☐	☐
b)	E-commerce provides opportunities for firms to move into foreign markets.	☐	☐
c)	Customers can search for products on a firm's website by using key words.	☐	☐
d)	There is no way to protect online customers from having their credit card details stolen.	☐	☐
e)	To get more business, firms often target foreign countries using online promotions.	☐	☐

Q3   Purrfect Catz Ltd. make cat accessories. They currently only sell their products in the UK. Explain how they could use the internet to expand their business.

....

....

....

....

....

Abraca-bloomin-dabra.

Q4   Two students have answered the following exam question. Who gives the better answer? Explain your reasoning.

Casual Knitz Ltd. are a mail order clothing business. They send catalogues to their customers four times a year. Explain how they could use e-commerce to reduce their business costs.

Casual Knitz could put all their products online on their website. The customers could search for products and order things that way instead. Or customers could download catalogues from the website too. They could show lots more products that way and send more regular updates by e-mail.

Vijay

Instead of sending catalogues to their customers, Casual Knitz could put this information online. This would save money, as Casual Knitz won't need to print and post catalogues. It would also mean customers would be able to buy online, which could automate a lot of the processes currently done by hand (e.g. writing address labels, processing payment), saving money. Casual Knitz could also email customers to let them know of new ranges, or of sales, saving postage costs.

Annette

Ahh yes, what I've done is forget to leave room for dots again. My bad.

E-commerce — shop till you Alt+F4...

Loads of people have now swapped the high street for the iStreet and shop online. I love it — no more being dragged round by my girlfriend while she goes in every clothes shop twice... ahem, sorry, got a bit distracted there — make sure you know all this real good, examiners love asking about this up to date stuff. Boo ya.

New Technology — E-Commerce

Q1 Tick the correct box to show how strongly you agree with each of these statements. Explain your answers as fully as you can.

	Strongly agree	Agree a little	Neither agree nor disagree	Disagree a little	Strongly disagree

a) Online technical support means companies no longer need a customer service department. ☐ ☐ ☐ ☐ ☐

....

....

b) For a business, one of the most important things about e-commerce is that it can reduce costs. ☐ ☐ ☐ ☐ ☐

....

....

c) For a business, the benefits of e-commerce are huge. ☐ ☐ ☐ ☐ ☐

....

....

d) E-commerce has very few disadvantages for customers. ☐ ☐ ☐ ☐ ☐

....

....

Q2 Explain how running a website can be expensive and time-consuming for a business.

....

....

....

Q3 Calvin wants to set up a small business selling DJ equipment online. He has been advised to spend time testing his website thoroughly before making it available for customers to use.

Pump up the volume along with the tempo

Suggest why thorough testing is important for Calvin.

....

....

....

....

Growth of Firms — Internal Expansion

Q1 Explain what each of the following mean, and why they might provide a small firm with an incentive to expand.

a) Economies of scale ....

....

b) Diversification ....

....

c) Financial security ....

....

d) Domination of the market ....

....

Q2 Which of the following is **not** an example of internal expansion? Tick the correct answer.

a) Producing more of the same product to sell in existing markets. ☐

b) Buying a competitor and selling its products in existing markets. ☐

c) Producing a new product and selling it in new markets. ☐

d) Targeting new markets in which to sell existing products. ☐

Ben could feel the internal expansion happening already.

Q3 Explain the difference between **line extension** and **diversification**.

....

....

....

Q4 Write down one advantage and one drawback to small firms of internal expansion.

Advantage ....

....

Drawback ....

....

Internal expansion — the result of too many tea breaks...

The key point on this page is that there are various reasons why internal expansion can be good for a firm. Make extra sure that you remember that internal expansion is all about firms expanding their own activities.

Growth of Firms — External Expansion

Q1   Explain how each of the following methods of external expansion can have **advantages** for the firm or firms involved.

Method of external expansion	Advantage
Joining with a competitor	....
Joining with an unrelated firm	....
Taking over a customer	....
Joining with a supplier	....

Q2   Explain how takeovers and mergers can cause problems for businesses.

....

....

....

....

Q3   Which of the following is **not** a benefit to a business of growing through franchising?

a)   Because other people are running parts of their business, the firm can grow without the extra cost of increased wages. ☐

b)   The company can grow without having to make difficult decisions about its general direction or whether it should introduce any new products. ☐

c)   The firm doesn't have to take on any of the usual costs or risks of opening a new outlet. ☐

d)   The business can rapidly increase their market share and awareness of their brand. ☐

Did someone say our name?

I thought they said French eyes...

I definitely heard something.

Is that your hand or mine?

A takeover could make your firm look 10 years younger...

It's not all fun and games with takeovers and mergers you know. Once I worked in a firework factory that was taken over by a company that made matches — oooh the sparks flew that day, let me tell you.

Effects of Expansion on Stakeholders

Q1 Complete the table below to show the effects of growth on a firm's stakeholders, and how those stakeholders might react to protect their interests.

Stakeholder	How are they affected?	How might they react?
Shareholders		
Employees		
Government		
Suppliers		
Local Community		
Customers		

Business Ownership Structures

Q1 Tick whether each of the following statements is true or false.

	True	False
a) Private limited companies can only sell new shares if all current shareholders agree.	☐	☐
b) Public limited companies have Ltd. after their name.	☐	☐
c) A public limited company is automatically formed when a private limited company has a certain number of shareholders.	☐	☐
d) Public limited companies tend to have access to more money to fund expansion.	☐	☐
e) Shares in public limited companies can be bought and sold by anybody.	☐	☐

Q2 Explain what is meant by "the divorce of ownership and control". Why can this become a problem for a business?

....
....
....

Q3 Explain how the objectives of a business may change as it grows.

....
....
....

Q4 Read the text below and then answer the question that follows.

Blackwell's Pies Ltd. is a private limited company started 15 years ago by Keith Blackwell. The company makes pies for many of the leading supermarket chains. Currently, all the shares in the company are held by Mr. Blackwell and his family. The company has grown steadily since it was started and now the shareholders are considering becoming a public limited company.

Discuss the advantages and disadvantages of making Blackwell's Pies Ltd. a public limited company.

capital   expansion   diversification
control   take over   objectives

The words in the grey box would be really good stuff to talk about in your answer — plus in an exam they'd help you get loads of marks.

....
....

You can't possibly have run out of things to write about already. I don't believe you — grab some paper and carry on...

Privates limited — we'll have no rudery around here...

Remember... becoming a PLC can be good for a firm, but there are drawbacks too. Eeeh... nothing's ever simple, is it. Still... one day, you'll look back on all this and laugh. Perhaps not tomorrow though.

Social Influences

Q1 Businesses can have **social** benefits. Describe **two** benefits that businesses can bring to society.

1. ....

2. ....

Q2 Some people claim that businesses selling alcohol are harming not just individuals, but society as a whole. Outline an argument that could be used to back up this claim.

....

....

....

....

Think about how alcohol can indirectly affect people who never even drink the stuff.

Q3 Explain how some businesses are now responding to the problems listed below.

Problem	Response to problem
Climate change	....
Depletion of resources	....
Exploitation of developing countries	....

Q4 Explain how taking ethical and environmental issues seriously can both have **benefits** and **drawbacks** for a business.

Here at Ray's, we do our bit for the environment by disposing of nuclear waste in all our burgers. We've won awards for our fusion cooking.

....

....

....

....

Q5 Greenpeace is a **pressure group** that campaigns against businesses it feels are not environmentally responsible. Explain how Greenpeace might reduce the profitability of a business that it targets.

....

....

Multinational Firms

Q1 Explain what is meant by a firm being 'multinational'.

....

Q2 Describe **two** ways that a firm can benefit from becoming a multinational enterprise (MNE).

1. ....

....

2. ....

....

Q3 Which of the following is **not** a potential benefit of MNEs to the host country?

a) MNEs are a source of investment and create employment for locals. ☐

b) The government of the host country receives revenue from taxes on the firm's profits. ☐

c) The MNEs pass on the benefits of their economies of scale to local businesses. ☐

d) The host country gets access to foreign technology and working methods. ☐

e) Export revenue from MNE sales abroad can improve the country's balance of payments. ☐

Q4 Describe **three** problems that MNEs can cause in the countries where they operate.

1. ....

....

2. ....

....

3. ....

....

Q5 Two students have answered an exam question.
Read their answers and then answer the question that follows.

Do you think MNEs are a positive thing for the host countries they operate in?
Give reasons for your answer.

MNEs are bad for a host country. They do what's best for themselves and do not worry about the countries they operate in. I think the host countries would be better off if the MNEs remained in their native countries.

Sarah

I think that overall, MNEs are not a positive thing. Although they do often benefit the countries that they operate in, the MNEs aim to benefit their shareholders more and will often achieve this by having a negative effect on the host country e.g. by causing environmental degradation.

Jason

Who do you think has given the better answer to the question? Explain your reasoning.

It's the <u>explain</u> bit of this question that's really important.

Product — The Product Life Cycle

Q1 The diagram below shows the sales of a product during its life cycle. Match each stage to the words in the box below.

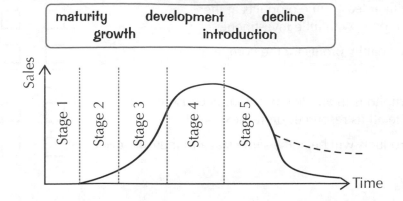

maturity   development   decline
growth   introduction

Stage 1: ....

Stage 2: ....

Stage 3: ....

Stage 4: ....

Stage 5: ....

Q2 Describe what marketing activities are most likely to be taking place during the following stages of a product's life cycle.

a) Development: ....

....

b) Introduction: ....

....

c) Decline: ....

....

Q3 A PC games manufacturer's portfolio includes 'Fantasy Soccer XI 2010' and '1001 Tricky Puzzles'. Tick whether you think the following statements are **true** or **false**.

True   False

a) The products' life cycles will be identical as long as they are launched together. ☐ ☐

b) The marketing mix for the puzzle game will probably change during its life cycle. ☐ ☐

c) The demand for both products will change over time. ☐ ☐

d) 'Fantasy Soccer XI 2010' will probably have a sales life of at least two years. ☐ ☐

Q4 A product will generate different cash-flows at different stages of its life cycle.

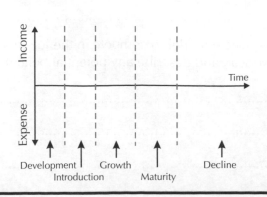

a) Draw a curve on these axes to show the cash-flows a business might expect from one of its products at the five stages shown.

b) How would your curve change if the business used an extension strategy as sales started to decline? Draw a dotted line to show the difference.

Product — Product Portfolios

Q1 A **product portfolio** is the range of products that a business sells.
Are the following statements true or false? Tick the correct boxes.

	True	False
a) A business aims to have a portfolio with at least some products at the peak of their sales, bringing in lots of money with little investment.	☐	☐
b) Products under development generate healthy profits for the company.	☐	☐
c) Large firms usually aim to have products at different stages of their product life cycles.	☐	☐
d) A firm with just one product in its portfolio is in an ideal position, because when sales start to decline, it can concentrate all its resources on its next product.	☐	☐
e) In a balanced product portfolio, all products will be at the same stage in their life cycles.	☐	☐

Q2 RSI Gaming Ltd. make games consoles. One of their products, the AddictaBox, is in the decline phase of its life cycle.

a) Explain what is meant by an **extension strategy**.
Suggest a suitable extension strategy RSI Gaming could use with the AddictaBox.

....

....

....

b) Describe a potential drawback to RSI Gaming of using an extension strategy.

....

....

Q3 Awoocar are a car company. They currently only make one model of car. It is a small car with a one-litre engine, and is available in four colours.

I'm afraid this is our only model, Madam.

Hmm, I was looking for something a tad bigger...but I'll take it.

a) One of Awoocar's directors wants to expand the company's portfolio by increasing the options available for the existing model (e.g. offer engines of different sizes, a greater range of colours etc.). Describe some pros and cons of this approach.

....

....

....

b) Another director wants the company to develop a completely new model to compete in the luxury car market. Explain why this approach might be riskier for Awoocar, and describe any potential benefits.

....

....

....

Price — Pricing Strategies

1 Match each pricing strategy below to its correct definition by drawing a line.

a) Firms charge the same prices as other firms who sell similar products.

b) A low price is charged to get consumers interested in the product. When sales increase the price is raised.

c) A new product is sold at a high price to make the product seem desirable. The price is then lowered to make it a mass-market product.

penetration pricing

price skimming

competitive pricing

Q2 TechyTech Ltd. is marketing their new type of 'e-paper'. This is a flexible sheet that can display electronic text and images without being lit from behind. Users can download books, newspapers and magazines onto a single device.

a) TechyTech decide to launch the product at a price that is much higher than their costs. What is the name of this pricing strategy?

....

b) What kind of customers might be prepared to pay a high price for this product at launch? Explain why.

....

....

c) Six months after the launch, TechyTech decides to reduce the price of its e-paper by 30%. Suggest a reason for this decision.

....

....

Q3 A firm decides to use **cost-plus** pricing for two of its products.

a) Calculate the selling price for each product using a percentage **mark-up**.

	Cost of making the product	% mark-up	Selling price
Product 1	£100	20%	
Product 2	£60	25%	

b) Calculate the selling price for each product using a percentage **profit margin**.

	Cost of making the product	% profit margin	Selling price
Product 1	£100	20%	
Product 2	£60	25%	

Promotion

Q1 Write a description of each of the sales promotion methods below.

a) BOGOF ....

....

b) point-of-sale advertising ....

....

c) product trial ....

....

Q2 A nightclub sends letters to GCSE students inviting them to celebrate their 16th birthdays at the club's 16-18's night. The letter includes vouchers that give money off non-alcoholic drinks at the bar.

a) Sending promotional material straight to potential customers is called **direct marketing**. What advantages does direct marketing have over other methods of promotion?

....

....

b) Explain the possible **disadvantages** of direct marketing for a business.

....

....

Q3 Osman is the manager of a garage in Troychester. He decides to promote his business by sponsoring a local tennis tournament.

> If your car needs a service, Osman's is ace!
> ...
> Can I go home now? This pose is really tiring.

a) Explain what it means for a business to sponsor an event.

....

....

....

b) Give one way that Osman's business might benefit from sponsoring the tennis tournament.

....

....

I asked my boss for a promotion — she told me to BOGOF...

Those pesky businesses — always finding sneaky ways to promote their products. Make sure you know the methods that businesses use. You have been reading about promotion, sponsored by Church Ladies' biscuits.

Place — Where the Product is Sold

1 The route a product takes from its manufacturer to the consumer is called its **distribution channel**. Which **two** of the following statements are true?

a) Retailers specialise in selling directly to consumers. ☐

b) Manufacturers never sell directly to consumers. ☐

c) Wholesalers buy products from a range of retailers. ☐

d) Most types of distribution channel are indirect. ☐

e) Wholesalers are involved in every type of distribution channel. ☐

Get your revision guides, madam — hot off the press from the manufacturer.

Bit of a flash sales pitch...

Q2 One distribution channel for products is **manufacturer — wholesaler — retailer — consumer**.

a) Give **two ways** that a manufacturer might benefit from selling its products to a wholesaler.

1. ....

2. ....

b) Give **two ways** that a retailer might benefit from buying products from a wholesaler.

1. ....

2. ....

Q3 Many manufacturers now sell their products to retailers, avoiding the use of a wholesale business in the distribution channel. Write down one benefit and one drawback that this might have **for the retailer**.

a) Benefit: ....

....

b) Drawback: ....

....

Q4 Lisa is setting up a small business selling hand-made cushions and other small furniture accessories. She has a part-time job in a local craft shop, and wants to earn some extra income from her hobby. She designs and makes each product herself — on average, she can produce three items per day.

a) Give **two** reasons why selling to a wholesaler would not be suitable for Lisa's business.

1. ....

2. ....

b) Recommend a distribution channel that might be suitable for Lisa's business, and explain your answer.

Recommended channel: ....

Explanation: ....

....

Sources of Finance — Large Firms

Q1 What are fixed assets? How can a firm use redundant fixed assets as a source of finance?

....

....

Q2 A large firm needs finance to buy 10 new computers.
Explain why issuing shares would not be the best way to finance the new computers.

....

....

Q3 Which **two** of the following are the most likely reasons why the owners of a large company might decide to use retained profits as a source of finance, rather than taking out a bank loan?

a) The firm is under pressure to pay out large dividends to shareholders. ☐

b) The company has recently issued more shares. ☐

c) They only need a relatively small amount of money. ☐

d) They need the money for a long period of time. ☐

e) They want to avoid paying interest on any money that they need. ☐

Q4 Explain how interest rates could affect a firm's choice of finance.

....

....

Q5 Three students have answered the following exam question — their answers are shown below. Who gives the best answer? Explain your reasoning.

> Cheese-a-rama Ltd, a large established frozen pizza manufacturer, is looking for a large amount of short-term finance. Recommend two possible sources of finance for Cheese-a-rama. Explain the reasons for your recommendations.

They could take out a bank loan because they are a big firm, so it would be quite easy. They could sell some things that they don't need any more, like old machines, and get money that way.

Helena

They could use internal finances, like retained profits, which they don't have to pay back. They could also take out a bank loan. They would have to pay it back with interest, but it would be a quick and easy way to get a lot of money.

Andy

The company could issue new shares. This money would not have to be repaid, unlike a loan. They could sell any fixed assets that they no longer use. This could get them quite a bit of money.

Simon

.... gives the best answer because ....

....

....

The Trading, Profit and Loss Account

Q1 Explain what a trading, profit and loss account records.

....

....

Q2 Why might it be useful for a business to compare profit and loss accounts from two consecutive years?

....

....

Q3 Identify **three** groups of people who might be interested in looking at a firm's profit and loss account. Give a reason for each.

Group	Reason
....	....
....	....
....	....

Q4 Study the profit and loss accounts below. Use them to help you answer the question that follows.

Trading, Profit and Loss Account
Jack Horner's Pies Ltd.
Year ending 31st March 2008

	£m
Turnover...............................	713
Cost of sales:	
Opening stock........ 45	
Purchases............. 390	
435	
Minus closing stock........ 75	
Cost of sales = ...	360
Gross profit =.....................	353
Minus expenses	
Wages and salaries.. 90	
Rent and rates........ 65	
Office expenses...... 30	
Advertising............. 12	
Depreciation........... 24	
Other expenses....... 31	
Expenses = ...	252
Operating profit = ...	101
Interest payable	15
Profit before tax (Net profit)...	86
Taxation	12.9
Dividends	18
Retained profit	55.1

Trading, Profit and Loss Account
Jack Horner's Pies Ltd.
Year ending 31st March 2009

	£m
Turnover...............................	689
Cost of sales:	
Opening stock........ 75	
Purchases............. 320	
395	
Minus closing stock........ 25	
Cost of sales = ...	370
Gross profit =.....................	319
Minus expenses	
Wages and salaries.. 65	
Rent and rates........ 65	
Office expenses...... 20	
Advertising............. 10	
Depreciation........... 30	
Other expenses....... 24	
Expenses = ...	214
Operating profit = ...	105
Interest payable	15
Profit before tax (Net profit)...	90
Taxation	13.5
Dividends	18
Retained profit	58.5

Try comparing the figures for 2008 and 2009 for these headings...

turnover

gross profit

wages

expenses

net profit

Hmm, tricky — two possible answers. Backing up your answer means you'll still get lots of juicy exam marks, whichever you pick.

Do you think Jack Horner's Pies Ltd. were performing better on 31st March 2008 or 31st March 2009?   Justify your answer.

Unless you have tiny writing and an even tinier pen, you'll need to answer this on a separate piece of paper.

Profitability Ratios

Q1 Businesses often calculate their **gross profit** and their **net profit**.

a) Explain the difference between these two types of profit.

....

....

b) Write down the formulas for calculating **gross profit margin** and **net profit margin**.

Gross profit margin = ... Net profit margin = ...

Q2 Use the information below to answer the questions that follow.

Sales £20,000, gross profit £7000, total expenses £5000.

a) Calculate the gross profit margin and the net profit margin.

Gross profit margin = ...

Net profit margin = ...

b) Explain what your answers to part a) mean in terms of money coming into the firm.

....

....

....

Q3 Use the information below to decide whether each of the following statements is true or false.

2007: sales £112,000, net profit £11,000, capital employed £130,000
2008: sales £132,000, net profit £18,000, capital employed £200,000

		True	False
a)	Sales revenue increased by 15.15% from 2007 to 2008.	☐	☐
b)	The net profit margin in 2008 was 7.33%.	☐	☐
c)	From 2007 to 2008, capital employed increased by 35%.	☐	☐
d)	The net profit margin in 2008 was greater than in 2007.	☐	☐

Q4 If a firm increases its prices (but costs do **not** rise), then its sales and gross profit **may fall**.
However, its **gross profit margin** will definitely **increase**.
Explain why you can be certain that gross profit margin will increase.

....

....

....

The Balance Sheet — Net Assets

Q1   Which of the following statements about balance sheets are **false**?

   a)   It shows what a business has done with its money. ☐

   b)   It shows whether a business has made a profit or a loss. ☐

   c)   It is used to calculate how much corporation tax a business needs to pay. ☐

   d)   It shows where a business got its money from. ☐

Q2   What does it mean to describe one type of current asset as **more liquid** than another?

....

....

Q3   A sole trader who has been trading for one year must now produce a balance sheet for his Bank Manager. Fill in the gaps below to complete his balance sheet.

BALANCE SHEET J. LOGAN – TIMBER TRADING, March 31, 2009	
Fixed Assets	**£**
Machinery	2840.00
Van	<u>3500.00</u>
	....
Current Assets	
Stock	1150.00
Debtors	3517.00
Cash in hand	<u>2118.00</u>
	....
Current Liabilities	
Creditors	2242.00
Bank Overdraft	<u>1383.00</u>
	....
Working Capital	....
Net Assets	....
Financed by	
Owners' Capital	4000.00
Enterprise Start-up grant	<u>2500.00</u>
	....
Bank Loan	3000.00
Capital Employed	....

Balance sheets — not as difficult as plate spinning...

In the exam you might be expected to interpret balance sheets — so make sure you're really happy with what all the different headings mean. Another page done and dusted. A bit like my best china. Hmph.

48

The Balance Sheet — Capital Employed

Q1 Explain the difference between current liabilities and long-term liabilities on a balance sheet.

....

....

Q2 Explain how each of the following can be a source of finance for a business.

a) Share capital: ....

....

....

b) Retained profits and reserves: ....

....

....

Q3 Which **two** of these statements are not true?

a) Net assets show what a company has done with its money (e.g. buying premises). ☐

b) Debentures are an example of a current liability. ☐

c) Capital employed is equal to the shareholders funds added to the long-term liabilities. ☐

d) Long-term liabilities do not include bank loans. ☐

e) Capital employed is the total money put into a business. ☐

f) Retained profits are profits that are kept instead of being paid out as dividends. ☐

Q4 Explain why a firm's capital employed must always be equal to its net assets.

....

....

....

Q5 Explain how a firm's stakeholders may use the balance sheet to assess the health of the business.

....

....

....

Stakeholder — a convenient place to store your rump...

Phew, it's all over. That page had lots of writing — a bit like an exam. Ick. The most important thing to remember is that capital employed must always be the same as net assets. Job's a good'un.

Liquidity Ratios

Q1 Explain why liquidity ratios might be useful to a business.

....

....

Q2 Using the information below, work out the current ratio for 2007 and 2008.

> 2007: current assets £16,000, current liabilities £12,000
> 2008: current assets £10,000, current liabilities £9500

....

....

2007 current ratio = ... 2008 current ratio = ...

Q3 Which of these statements about the current ratio is **not** true?

a) It shows whether the firm has enough money to pay this year's debts. ☐

b) A figure below 1 means a firm might not be able to pay its bills. ☐

c) It assumes the firm won't be able to turn stock into cash during the year. ☐

d) An ideal figure would be around 1.5. ☐

e) A ratio above 2 may mean the firm could invest some of its money more profitably. ☐

Q4 Using the information below, work out the acid test ratio for 2007 and 2008.

> **2007**: stock = £4500; cash = £3500; debtors = £2000; current liabilities £11,750
> **2008**: stock = £3300; cash = £7000; debtors = £2900; current liabilities £10,600

....

....

2007 acid test ratio = ... 2008 acid test ratio = ...

Q5 Look at the two acid test ratios above. In which year was the business in a better position to pay off its debts? Justify your answer.

....

....

Woah, I am currently a liability in these new heels...

Current ratio, acid test ratio — they aren't the catchiest of names. But make sure you know what they show, and how you work them out, inside out. I'm off to find some ankle supports. Or a stretcher.

Analysis of Accounts

Q1 Draw lines to join each term to its description on the right.

| Current ratio | Fraction of each £1 spent by a customer not used to make the product. |

Net profit margin — Proportion of current liabilities that could be met by current assets.

Gross profit margin — Fraction of each £1 spent by a customer left as profit after all costs are paid.

Acid test ratio — Proportion of current liabilities that could be met by current assets (not including stock).

Q2 Explain why it might be useful to compare ratios from different years.

....

....

Q3 Study the trading, profit and loss account and balance sheet below.

EI'S PIES — TRADING, PROFIT AND LOSS ACCOUNT
Year ending 31 March 2009

	£	£
Sales		50,000
Purchases	30,000	
Gross profit		20,000
Expenses	18,000	
Net profit		2000

Why not use this handy space for your working out...

EI'S PIES — BALANCE SHEET
Dated 31 March 2009

	£	£
Fixed Assets:		
Premises		6900
Machinery		2500
Van		3200
		12,600
Current Assets:		
Stock	1560	
Debtors	5500	
Cash in hand	300	
	7360	
Current Liabilities:		
Creditors	1700	
Bank overdraft	60	
	1760	
Working Capital:		5600
Net Assets:		18,200
Financed by:		
Owners' Capital		16,200
Net Profit		2000
Capital Employed:		18,200

Use the above information to work out the following:

a) Gross profit margin = ... %

b) Net profit margin = ... %

c) Current ratio = ...

d) Acid test ratio = ...

Q4 Comment on the ratios for Ei's Pies. Highlight any concerns the owners of this business might have and suggest what they could do about them.

Use a chisel to engrave your answer on a stone tablet. Or use a pen and a spare piece of paper.

Organisational Structure

Q1   Read the following description of a business, and answer the questions below.

> Eggeds is a private limited company that sells graphical calculators.
> The company has four directors, each in charge of one functional area:
> marketing, finance, administration and production. Each director reports
> to the managing director of the company. Within their own functional
> area, each director is responsible for the work of two managers.

a)   Based on the description of Eggeds, how would you expect the company to be organised
— by function, product or region? Justify your answer.

....

b)   In the space below, draw an organisational chart for the company which includes all of the employees
mentioned above.

Q2   Complete the table below to show an advantage and
a disadvantage of each organisational structure.

Organise by...	Advantage	Disadvantage
Function		
Product		
Region		

Organisational Structure

CAUTION
WET
PAINT

Higher, Archie!

Q1 Explain what is meant by a **hierarchy** in a business.

....

....

....

Q2 Tick whether each of the following statements is **true** or **false**.

		True	False
a)	Generally, the number of people at each level decreases as you move up a hierarchy.	☐	☐
b)	People in one layer of a hierarchy have authority over people in the levels above.	☐	☐
c)	All new employees in a business start in the bottom level of the hierarchy, and must work their way up.	☐	☐
d)	In every business, the people in the top layer of the hierarchy have no input into the day-to-day running of the firm.	☐	☐

Q3 Draw lines to join each term with its description on the right.

Centralised Organisation

Decentralised Organisation

All major decisions are made by one person or a few senior managers at the top of the hierarchy.

The authority to make most decisions is shared out between workers.

Q4 Discuss the drawbacks to a business of having a **decentralised** structure.

....

....

....

Q5 Describe how the structure of a business may change as it grows and the problems this can cause. Explain what action the business can take to try to overcome these problems.

These would be good things to talk about in your answer.

No room here I'm afraid — you'll have to write your answer somewhere else. Unless you write really small, and can squeeze it in here —> ....

hierarchy   costs   decisions
responsibility   delayering

Centralisation — sounds pretty middle of the road to me...

If you haven't got the joke at the top of the page, have a look — it's a beaut. As for the rest of the page, make sure you can do all these questions in your sleep, cos there's bound to be something like one of them on the exam.

Effects of Expansion — Communication

Q1 Kevin is a department manager for Dewy, Robbem & Howe, a financial services company. He has a span of control of 12 workers.

a) What does the term 'span of control' mean?

....

....

b) Explain why having a wide span of control can be a problem for a business.

....

....

....

Q2 Which of the following statements are **not** true?

a) A firm with four layers in its hierarchy has three people in its longest chain of communication. ☐

b) Large firms tend to be more hierarchical than small firms. ☐

c) Directors and shareholders are found at the top of a firm's chain of command. ☐

d) As a firm becomes more hierarchical, it loses layers of management. ☐

Q3 Outdaws & Son Ltd. make play equipment for gardens. They have a chain of stores across the UK. Part of the firm's hierarchy is shown to the right.

a) A director feels the firm's chains of communication have become too long. Describe some problems with long chains of communication.

....

....

....

Outdaws & Son Ltd.

Ron D. Bowt
UK Sales Director
↓
Hector Skelter
Regional Sales Manager
↓
Sue Wings
District Sales Manager
↓
C. Soar
Branch Sales Manager
↓
Mikey Barrs
Branch Sales Supervisor
↓
Sandy Pitt
Salesperson

b) What is meant by **de-layering**? Which employees of Outdaws & Son do you think would be most affected if the firm decided to de-layer its hierarchy?

....

....

....

....

Have you seen the latest projections for the third quarter retail sales?

No, what's the worst case, going forward?

If you can't hear what I'm saying, raise your hand...

If a large firm has a breakdown in communication, it can cause massive problems.
Here at CGP we communicate using a foolproof combination of semaphore and trained postal gerbils.

Staff Training

Q1 Most businesses give their employees **induction training**.

a) When does induction training occur? Tick the correct box.

i) (Throughout a worker's employment. ☐)   ii) (At the start of a worker's employment. ☐)

iii) (Whenever a new skill needs to be learned. ☐)

b) Explain the main purposes of induction training.

....

....

Q2 Many businesses give their staff **on-the-job** training. Write down one advantage and one disadvantage that this training method can have for a business.

Advantage: ....

Disadvantage: ....

Q3 SilkiSoft is a company that produces videogames. It sometimes sends its programming staff to courses at a local university to learn new skills.

LECTURE OVER
Save and continue
Save and quit
▶ Quit job (don't save)

a) What is the name of training that takes place outside the business?

....

b) How might SilkiSoft's staff benefit from being trained at the university rather than at work?

....

c) Give one disadvantage to SilkiSoft of training its staff away from the workplace.

....

Q4 Many businesses use a system of **appraisals** (or **performance reviews**) as part of staff training.

a) Briefly explain how the appraisal process works. Use some or all of the words in the box in your answer.

employee   manager   training   targets   performance

....

....

....

b) Describe two possible problems that can occur with appraisals.

1. ....

2. ....

Staff Motivation and Retention

Q1 Explain what is meant by **remuneration**.

....

....

> C'mon lads. The faster you are, the quicker you'll find my...erm, your remuneration.

Q2 Explain how staff can be motivated by being given the opportunity to learn new skills.

....

....

....

Q3 Meera is the manager of a shoe shop. She employs twelve members of staff, but does not consult them about the decisions she makes as a manager.

a) What is the name of Meera's management style? Tick the correct box.

Paternalistic ☐   Laissez-faire ☐   Authoritarian ☐   Democratic ☐

b) Why might this management style damage the motivation of some members of staff?

....

....

....

Q4 Four Walls Ltd. operate a chain of estate agents around the country. They employ a large number of workers, but struggle to keep employees for more than a couple of years.

a) Explain why staff retention is important for businesses.

....

....

b) Describe one method large businesses use to try to retain staff.

....

....

....

Poor motivation? Try revising your expectations...

When you're revising for exams, it can be tough to stay motivated. But remember — motivation comes from within. That's not very helpful, but it might come up in the exam. Er, good luck. *Runs away*

Specialisation and Interdependence

Q1   Explain how specialisation may be used within a business and how it might affect efficiency.

....

....

....

Q2   Tick whether you think the following statements about specialisation are true or false.

		True	False
a)	Workers get more efficient at their task.	☐	☐
b)	Workers improve their skills.	☐	☐
c)	It usually means that a firm's output is reduced	☐	☐
d)	It is also called division of labour.	☐	☐
e)	It involves workers rotating around different tasks.	☐	☐

This division of labour has ruined another good shirt.

Q3   Write down **three** ways in which the division of labour can lead to problems.

1. ....

2. ....

3. ....

Q4   Draw a production chain for a jar of coffee. Use the words in the box to help you draw the chain.

distribution company	coffee factory	retailer
processor	shipping agent	grower

Q5   What would be the effect on the firms in the production chain above if the coffee grower's crops failed?

....

....

....

Methods of Production

Q1 Flow production is one method used to manufacture goods.

a) Explain what is meant by **flow production**.

....

....

b) Which of these products would you expect to be made by flow production? Tick your answer(s).

bridges	televisions	mobile phones	ships	chocolate bars
☐	☐	☐	☐	☐

Q2 Which of these statements about flow production are true?

a) Modern flow production methods achieve maximum efficiency by increasing the workforce. ☐

b) The aim of flow production is to benefit from specialisation and economies of scale. ☐

c) Flow production is the opposite of mass production. ☐

d) Flow production is highly capital intensive. ☐

Q3 Describe one potential disadvantage of a mechanised production line to make products for a rapidly changing market.

....

....

....

Q4 The managers of a furniture manufacturer that currently uses job production announce that, to improve efficiency, they want to switch to flow production. Explain why employees might be concerned.

....

....

....

Flow, flow, flow your product, gently down the machine...

Flow production might sound like hard work for all those machines. But don't worry, I hear that it rocks their cogs*. Make sure you know what flow production is and the effect it can have on a firm's efficiency.

Productivity

Q1 Look at the stock control graph below for Chuck Wagon Burgers.

a) What is the re-order level for the burgers?

....

b) What is the minimum number of burgers they should have in stock?

....

c) How many burgers are there in each order?

....

d) How long does it take for each order to arrive?

....

e) Explain how Chuck Wagon Burgers could use computers to help with their stock control.

....

Q2 Give **one** advantage and **one** disadvantage of the 'Just-in-case' method of stock control.

Advantage: ....

....

Disadvantage: ....

....

Q3 Which of these is **not** a feature of lean production? Tick your answer.

a) Workers are encouraged to think about ways to improve their productivity. ☐

b) Waste and stocks of raw materials are kept to a minimum. ☐

c) It aims to use as few resources as possible. ☐

d) Stock levels of resources are kept high in order to increase production. ☐

Q4 Sometimes a business has to rationalise its operations to increase efficiency. List three actions that it might take in order to achieve this.

1. ....

2. ....

3. ....

Q5 Cheap as Chips Ltd. make computers. They are thinking of switching to the "Just-in-time" method of stock control in their factories. Discuss the implications of using this method of production.

Ahh, looks like I've run out of space. No worries, I'm sure you'll have some paper nearby 'just-in-case'. Now would be an ideal time to use it.

Effects of Expansion — Economies of Scale

Q1   Which of the following is the correct description of the term 'economy of scale'?

a)   The reduction in corporation tax that a large business has to pay to the government.   ☐

b)   The reduction in total costs that results from operating a business on a larger scale.   ☐

c)   The reduction in average costs that results from operating a business on a larger scale.   ☐

d)   The increase in profits available to large businesses from charging more for their products.   ☐

Q2   Write a description of each of the internal economies of scale given below.

a)   Marketing economies ....
....

b)   Financial economies ....
....

c)   Technical economies ....
....

d)   Risk-bearing economies ....
....

Q3   Read the text below and then answer the question that follows.

> Fission Chips is the latest in a long line of high-tech firms to locate in the 'Silicon Dale' area of north-west Yorkshire. The large number of such firms that have located in this area in the last 15 years has even led to the founding of a specialist college in the Dale, which hopes to train 'the Bill Gates of tomorrow' according to their website.

Explain how these developments might benefit firms located in the Silicon Dale area. Make sure you mention each of the groups of people in the box below.

workforce   suppliers   government

....
....
....
....
....

Q4   Explain one way in which the growth of a business can lead to **diseconomies** of scale.

....
....

Quality Management

Q1 Decide if each of the following is a characteristic of 'Quality control' (QC), 'Total Quality Management' (TQM), or both.

		QC	TQM
a)	Products are usually checked at several stages of the production process.	☐	☐
b)	There is an emphasis on after-sales service, as well as quality of production.	☐	☐
c)	The idea is to reduce waste and stop customers receiving faulty products.	☐	☐
d)	It is a culture of quality assurance — every employee is involved.	☐	☐
e)	Workers are often involved in quality circles to identify and solve problems.	☐	☐

Q2 Explain how TQM can lead to **both** the motivation **and** demotivation of workers.

....

....

....

Q3 Give **two** reasons why an expanding business might find it hard to maintain high quality.

1. ....

....

2. ....

....

Q4 Two students have answered the following exam question — their answers are shown below. Who gives the better answer? Explain your reasoning.

"Quality control" and "Total Quality Management" are methods used to ensure high quality standards. Which do you think would be more successful in improving quality throughout a business? Explain your answer.

I think TQM would be more successful because it encourages all workers to think of quality as their responsibility, and there's an emphasis on getting things right first time. Unlike quality control, which is mostly concerned with the quality of production, TQM looks at quality throughout the whole business, including things like customer service.

Michael

Quality control involves checking products to make sure quality standards are being met. Products are checked for things like design, appearance, defects and safety. TQM on the other hand is more of a 'culture of quality'.

Caley

.... gives the better answer because ....

....

....

I can't control the quality — it keeps getting free...

The bigger a firm gets, the harder it can be to maintain quality. Just remember that Total Quality Management is a culture of quality — it's every worker's responsibility to make sure the products are of a good standard.

Controlled Assessment

Research involves deciding how _believable_ sources of information are, and drawing _sensible conclusions_. Don't believe _everything_ you read. (E.g. apparently some things on the internet aren't actually true.)

For a lot of these questions, you're going to need to write your answers on separate sheets of paper. Best go get some now.

Q1 Below are some sources of information that you might be able to use while researching a project on businesses in your local area. Explain some of the pros and cons of each source. (E.g. would you expect the information to be accurate, up-to-date, useful... and so on.)

a) Book in local library — E.g. Businesses and services change quickly — a book might not have up-to-date info.
....

b) United Nations website
....

c) Local council website
....

d) Own knowledge
....

e) www.wikipedia.org
....

f) University website
....

Q2 Jessica is researching leisure facilities for young people in Darlyton Green. Read the info that Jessica has gathered. Then, based on that information, mark on the scales **how confident** you feel about the statements that follow, justifying your answers. _I did the first one to show you what I mean._

17th June 2002
'Bored' Youths Break New Church Windows

Police were called to St Mary's Church, Darlyton Green last night after a gang of youths smashed the church's new stained glass windows.
Parishioners had tirelessly fundraised for 2 years to raise money to replace the windows. Fr Lynch said "Groups of young people often hang around the church at night. There is nothing else for them to do in this area."

① Local newspaper

<u>RE: Is Darlyton Green the worst place to live in the UK???</u>
Posted by xcrazeeechick13x 19:03 10th May 2008.
I hate livin here!!! there is nothing to do at all :(

② Screenshot from social networking site.

Darlyton Green is a thriving community with excellent shopping, a variety of restaurants and a newly built state-of-the-art theatre, all catering for a rising population of 133,200.

③ Quote taken from tourism site for local area

Age group	Population Darlyton Green 2001
0-11	17,225
12-17	10,184
18-24	9,168
25-35	26,119
36-59	33,640
60+	23,598
Total	119,934

④ Census results

Confident it's false — Might be true — Confident it's true

a) The current population of Darlyton Green is greater than 100,000.
I reckon this is very likely to be true — the Census said the population was over 100,000 in 2001 (their figure was probably fairly accurate at the time). And according to the tourism site it's 133,200 and rising (which is _way_ over 100,000). So even though I wouldn't take the tourism site's word for this exact figure (they're not experts in statistics), a population over 100,000 seems a safe bet.

b) In 2001 there were exactly 27,409 people in Darlyton Green under the age of 18.

c) The current population of Darlyton Green is exactly 133,200.

d) Most under-18s are unhappy with the leisure facilities in Darlyton Green.

e) There is no shortage of leisure facilities for young people in Darlyton Green.

f) Darlyton Green has at least three fast-food restaurants.

Q3 Use whatever sources you like to find the following as accurately as you can.

a) the number of births in Scotland in 2008

b) the current population of London

c) the number of Mexican restaurants in Swansea

d) the % of the UK's population with internet access

Controlled Assessment

Very often, when you do research you end up with a <u>heap</u> of numbers. You need to get these numbers to "<u>say something useful</u>". See what useful information you can get from these jumbles of numbers...

Q1   The following information was gathered at Darlyton Green High School.

In 2008, 50 males and 50 females of each age were asked about what they did in their spare time. This table shows the results.

Number of pupils starting at Darlyton Green High School								
Year	2001	2002	2003	2004	2005	2006	2007	2008
M	101	107	105	105	123	124	128	127
F	84	92	91	93	103	108	112	115
Total	185	199	196	198	226	232	240	242

		No of people who answered yes (by age and gender)					
Do you...		11	12	13	14	15	16
Play sports	M	32	36	28	40	28	16
	F	20	12	24	32	24	12
Play an instrument	M	12	16	16	20	8	16
	F	16	24	16	12	12	20
Go to cafés	M	8	12	7	12	17	15
	F	24	30	22	24	29	36
Enjoy shopping	M	8	6	6	11	13	9
	F	29	33	39	40	40	32

a)   Using information from the tables, plot **one** of each of the following.

i)   a bar chart

ii)   a pie chart

iii)   a line graph

Bar charts and pie charts are good for comparing numbers. Line graphs show how things change over time.

b)   Use your graphs to draw a conclusion about the data.

c)   Use your answer to b) and your Business Studies knowledge to write down a potential business idea that could be aimed at the young people of Darlyton Green.

Don't worry about writing big long epic answers — scribble down any ideas that you might have. Mention your graphs in your notes to help back up your ideas.

You'll need to write a <u>report</u> for your controlled assessment, and this report needs to be <u>organised</u>. It's best to do it in <u>separate sections</u> so it's easier for the reader to understand.

Q2   Dave was asked to come up with a new business idea for his local area, aimed at young people. He has produced a report to explain his ideas.

Dave wrote a contents page for his report, which his younger sister then spilt black ink over (no... really).

Match each of the sections of his report below to its description.
Then suggest a suitable order for Dave's contents page. Explain why you've chosen this order.

Research methods:

Research results:

Summary of research:

Introduction:

Conclusion:

Recommendations:

• what Dave would suggest, based on his research results

• explanation of how Dave collected his data

• general explanation of how Dave's going to tackle the task

• graphs, tables, questionnaire data, information from books/internet etc.

• the overall 'story' that Dave thinks his research tells him

• limitations of Dave's research, other research he could have done

CONTENTS
1)
2)
3)
4)
5)
6)

Exam Marks

Marking other people's exam answers can help you see how easy it is to lose marks if you're not really careful. So have a look at the answers on these pages and be ready to play the part of an examiner...

Q1   Below are two students' answers (and marks) for the following question.

> What is meant by 'flow production'?   (2 marks)

> Flow production is when a firm makes lots of things at the same time. Robots often do a lot of the work, and cars are often made using flow production.   ①
>
> **Anita**

> Flow production is when a company makes many identical products, often on a production line. At each stage on a production line, a particular task is carried out.   ②
>
> **Rachel**

Why do you think Rachel was awarded more marks than Anita?

....

....

Q2   Read Jo's answer to the exam question below and answer the questions that follow.

> What is meant by 'span of control'?   (2 marks)

> In a hierarchy a number of workers will report to each manager. The number of workers reporting to a particular manager is that manager's span of control. The manager is responsible for passing on messages and looking after everyone in their span of control. If a span of control is too wide, it can take a long time for messages to reach all the workers and they might become demotivated. This can be bad for the business as productivity might be reduced.   ②

a)   Jo's answer was pretty good, but it **isn't perfect**. Are any parts of Jo's answer irrelevant? Cross out anything you think could be removed without affecting the mark.

b)   Jo said later that: *"It's best to write loads for each question, because that way you're bound to say the right thing eventually."* Is Jo right? Why might her strategy not be the best idea?

....

Examiners use mark schemes — these show examiners what they can give marks for. They're quite specific — you don't get marks for quantity, only quality. Have a look at this one...

Q3   Below is an exam question and its mark scheme, along with Gethin's answer.

> Explain what is meant by induction training.   (2 marks)

> Induction training means things like being told company rules and being taken on a tour of the worksite.

Mark Scheme

Description of answer	Marks
No valid response.	0
The answer **states** relevant point(s).	1
The answer **provides explanation** of point(s)	2

Use the mark scheme to mark Gethin's answer. Explain why you have given him the mark you have.

This answer gets ..... mark(s) out of 2 because ....

Exam Marks

Q1 Use the mark scheme given below to mark each part of Marie's answer. Explain why you have given her the mark you have.

Source 1
Abigail makes 40 pieces of jewellery a month and sells them online for £15 each. Each piece costs £4 to make and her website costs £110 a month to run.

Use the information in Source 1 to calculate Abigail's:
i)   monthly revenue (3 marks)
ii) monthly direct costs (3 marks)
iii) gross monthly profit (3 marks)
iv) net monthly profit (3 marks)

Show all your working out clearly.

Mark Scheme

Description of answer	Marks
No valid response.	0
The answer shows **understanding** of the **concept**.	1-2
The answer is **calculated correctly**.	3

Marie's answers

i) monthly revenue = sales × selling price
= 40 × £15 = £6000

ii) monthly direct costs
= sales × direct costs per item
= 40 × £4
= £160

iii) gross monthly profit
= revenue — direct costs
= £600 — £160
= £340

iv) net monthly profit
= revenue — indirect costs
= £600 — £110
= £490

i) This answer gets __2__ mark(s) out of 3 because
although the answer should be £600, Marie has used the correct formula — she just made a silly mistake when multiplying

ii) This answer gets .... mark(s) out of 3 because

iii) This answer gets .... mark(s) out of 3 because

iv) This answer gets .... mark(s) out of 3 because

Q2 Below is an exam question, its mark scheme, and Dan's answer.

Explain two factors that may determine where a new firm decides to locate. (4 marks)

A new firm might want to be close to their raw materials. They may also choose to locate in an area of high unemployment, as this means there will be lots of potential workers, and there may also be government grants available if the firm can provide employment.

Mark Scheme

Description of answer	Marks
No valid response.	0
The answer **identifies** factor(s) that may affect a firm's decision on where to locate.	1-2
The answer **explains** factor(s) that may affect a firm's decision on where to locate.	3-4

Use the mark scheme to mark Dan's answer. Explain why you have given him this mark.

This answer gets ...... mark(s) out of 4 because

Exam Marks

Writing long answers to essay-style questions is tricky. Marking them isn't the easiest thing in the world either, as you're about to find out. There are two mark schemes this time — and you need to use both.

Q1   Below is an exam question and Ellen's answer.

> The car manufacturer Kaori are launching a new small car. It has been designed with small families in mind, who need a reasonably spacious car with good fuel economy.
>
> i) Kaori are currently trying to decide on the elements of a promotional campaign for their new model. Recommend to the directors of Kaori some marketing activities they may wish to consider. Give reasons for your answer.   (9 marks)

Kaori will probably want to launch several different marketing activities. They will want as many people as possible to know that their new model has been launched, especially people with children, who are the target market. Adverts on TV and in newspapers and magazines would help with this. Adverts on billboards might also make lots of people aware of the Kaori brand relatively cheaply.

However, Kaori will probably need more than a 'general awareness' of their new product, they will want people who are about to buy a new car to consider Kaori's new model. People who are about to buy a car may well buy specialist car magazines, so Kaori should probably consider advertising there too.

They could also do some more unusual marketing activities to attract attention. For example they could organise competitions or raffles to win new cars in shopping centres, which would be very eye-catching. Or they could offer 20% discounts to the first 1000 customers to purchase the new model, which might encourage people to act quickly and sell some cars so that they are seen driving about, which might be useful marketing in itself.

This first mark scheme is used to assess a student's Business Studies knowledge, and their understanding of the scenario in the question.

Description of answer	Marks
No valid response.	0
The answer **states** relevant point(s).	1
The answer **provides explanation** of point(s)	2

a)   Use the mark scheme to mark Ellen's answer. Explain why you have given her this mark.

This answer gets .... mark(s) out of 2 because ....

....

This second mark scheme is used to assess a student's ability to analyse and evaluate evidence. It's also where you get marks for the "quality of written communication".

Description of Answer	Marks
The answer gives an **unsupported** judgement. Written communication is **simplistic,** and very few **technical terms** are correctly used.	1-2
The answer gives a judgement with **some** support and justification. Ideas are communicated with some **structure** and use of **technical terms** (though **some** may be used incorrectly).	3-5
Candidate offers judgement with **justification**. Ideas are communicated with a **clear structure** and correct use of **technical terms**.	6-7

b)   Re-read Ellen's answer. This time use this second mark scheme to give her a mark out of 7. Explain why you've given her this mark.

This answer gets .... mark(s) out of 2 because

....

....

Okay... you're hopefully nearly ready for the exam. But there's nowt like doing some exam-style questions to get you ready for the big day. That's why we've included a selection on the next few pages...

Sample Exam Questions

1   Read **Source 1** below and then answer the questions that follow.

> ### Source 1
> Jenny has decided to turn her hobby of making jewellery out of recyclable waste into a business. She will run the business as a sole trader and sell her items online through her own website. She has written a business plan and identified some business aims she would like to achieve in the first year.

(a)   What is meant by a 'sole trader'?

(2 marks)

(b)   Suggest **two** potential aims for Jenny's business.

(2 marks)

(c)   Explain **two** other ways Jenny could use computers and the internet to make her business more efficient.

(5 marks)

(d)   Jenny feels that good customer service is important if her business is to succeed.

Describe how good customer service can help Jenny's business become more profitable.

(7 marks)

2   Read **Source 2** below and then answer the questions that follow.

> ### Source 2
> Chris and James run a catering firm which supplies food for parties, weddings, and other special occasions.
>
> They currently employ 4 full-time staff, but are going to ask some of these to consider other work patterns.
>
> Currently Chris and James are struggling to pay outstanding debts with some of their suppliers.

(a)   State **two** different work patterns other than full-time.

(2 marks)

(b)   Chris and James need to improve the business's cash flow.

Explain how introducing different work patterns might help them achieve this.

(4 marks)

(c)   Chris and James want to make sure their staff are as well motivated as possible.

Discuss ways in which Chris and James could motivate their staff.

(6 marks)

3 Read **Source 3** below and then answer the questions that follow.

Source 3

Mel and Paul are two friends who are going to start out in business together. They are going to set up a new hairdressing salon as a partnership.

They have received an £8,000 loan from the bank, but they still need some additional funding.

(a) Identify **two** other sources of finance that Mel and Paul could consider applying for.

(2 marks)

(b) Explain **two** factors that may influence Mel and Paul's decision regarding the location of their salon.

(5 marks)

(c) Recommend **two** methods they could use to promote their shop. Give reasons for your answer.

(7 marks)

4 Read **Source 4** below and then answer the questions that follow.

Source 4

Raymer's Ltd. are a baked-bean manufacturer located on the outskirts of a large town. They use flow production to make their product and employ over 90 staff.

The firm's sales have grown each year and the directors are keen to diversify their business and continue its growth. There is a playing field located next to the factory that they are hoping to buy so that they can expand their factory.

(a) What is meant by diversification?

(2 marks)

(b) Identify one way in which Raymer's Ltd may be able to fund their expansion.

(2 marks)

(c) Describe the ways in which the firm's expansion might affect the local community.

(5 marks)

(d) The directors are concerned that the planned expansion may adversely affect the quality of their products.

Recommend one way in which the directors may be able to ensure that the quality of their products remains high.

(5 marks)

5   Read **Source 5** below and then answer the questions that follow.

Source 5

Extract of financial data for Yaleston Fashion Ltd.

	2007	2008
Sales revenue	£28m	£35m
Gross profit	£17m	£23m
Net profit	£3	£3.2m

(a) Use the information in **Source 5** to calculate the increase in gross profit between 2007 and 2008 for Yaleston Fashion Ltd.

(2 marks)

(b) Calculate the net profit margin for Yaleston Fashion for 2008.

Use the following formula: net profit margin $= \dfrac{\text{net profit}}{\text{sales revenue}} \times 100\%$

Show your workings.

(3 marks)

(c) (i)   Calculate the percentage change in gross profit.

(2 marks)

(ii) Calculate the percentage change in net profit.

(2 marks)

(d) Use this data to discuss whether Yaleston's Fashions Ltd. performed better in 2008 than it did in 2007.

(9 marks)

6   Read **Source 6** below and then answer the questions that follow.

Source 6

Dasha Fashion Ltd. are a clothes manufacturer with four factories in the UK. They want to expand by taking over one of their competitors, Clash Ltd, who have six factories in India.

After this takeover, Dasha will be looking to expand the business further by building two more factories abroad.

(a) Identify **two** possible advantages to Dasha of expanding.

(2 marks)

(b) Explain **two** potential advantages to Dasha of expanding abroad.

(5 marks)

(c) Discuss the possible effects on the host country of Dasha's two proposed factories.

(7 marks)

Assessment Skills